The Beat[les]

CW0066480

Guitar

Specially transcribed
by *Alan Warner*.

Intros

Wise Publications
London/New York/Paris/Sydney/Copenhagen/Madrid

Exclusive Distributors:
Music Sales Limited
8/9 Frith Street, London W1V 5TZ, England.
Music Sales Pty Limited
120 Rothschild Avenue, Rosebery, NSW 2018, Australia.

Order No. NO90565
ISBN 0-7119-3398-7
This book © Copyright 1995 by Wise Publications

Compiled by Pat Conway
Music transcribed by Alan Warner
Music processed by Seton Music Graphics
Book design by Niche
Text photographs courtesy of Pictorial Press and
London Features International

Cover design by Studio Twenty, London
Cover photographs courtesy of
London Features International and Leslie Bryce

Printed in the United Kingdom by
J.B. Offset Printers (Marks Tey) Limited, Marks Tey, Essex.

Your Guarantee of Quality

As publishers, we strive to produce every book to the
highest commercial standards.
The music has been freshly engraved and the book has been carefully designed to minimise
awkward page turns and to make playing from it a real pleasure.
Throughout, the printing and binding have been planned to ensure a sturdy, attractive
publication which should give years of enjoyment.
If your copy fails to meet our high standards, please inform us and we will gladly replace it.

Music Sales' complete catalogue describes thousands of titles and is available in
full colour sections by subject, direct from Music Sales Limited.
Please state your areas of interest and send a cheque/postal order for £1.50 for postage to:
Music Sales Limited, Newmarket Road, Bury St. Edmunds, Suffolk IP33 3YB.

1 A Hard Day's Night

SINGLE: A Hard Day's Night/Things We Said Today 10.7.1964
ALBUM: A Hard Day's Night 10.7.1964

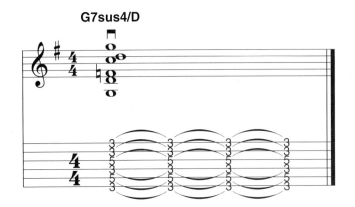

THE CHARTS   23 JULY 1964

1   A HARD DAY'S NIGHT   The Beatles
2   IT'S ALL OVER NOW   The Rolling Stones
3   I JUST DON'T KNOW WHAT TO DO WITH MYSELF   Dusty
       Springfield
4   I WON'T FORGET YOU   Jim Reeves
5   HOUSE OF THE RISING SUN   The Animals
6   CALL UP THE GROUPS   The Barron Knights
7   HOLD ME   P.J. Proby
8   ON THE BEACH   Cliff Richard
9   DO WAH DIDDY DIDDY   Manfred Mann
10 IT'S OVER   Roy Orbison

2 Day Tripper

SINGLE: We Can Work It Out/Day Tripper 3.12.1965

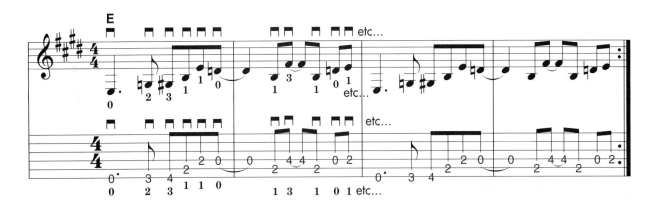

3 I Saw Her Standing There

ALBUM: Please Please Me 22.3.1963

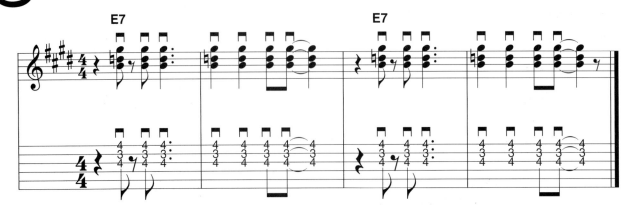

Day Tripper

E
Got a good reason for taking the easy way out,
A   E
Got a good reason for taking the easy way
out, now,
          F#7
She was a day tripper, one way ticket, yeh
          A7 G#7   C#7
It took me so long to find out,
                    B   E
and I found out.

She's a big teaser, she took me half the way there,
She's a big teaser, she took me half the way
there, now,
She was a day tripper, one way ticket, yeh,
It took me so long to find out,
and I found out.

Tried to please her, she only played one
night stands.
Tried to please her, she only played one
night stands, now,
She was a day tripper, Sunday driver, yeh,
It took me so long to find out,
and I found out.
Day tripper, day tripper, yeh.
Day tripper, day tripper, yeh.

Fade.

THE CHARTS   16 DECEMBER 1965

1 DAY TRIPPER/WE CAN WORK IT OUT   The
   Beatles
2 THE CARNIVAL IS OVER   The Seekers ....
3 WIND ME UP (LET ME GO)   Cliff Richard ....
4 1-2-3   Len Barry.................
5 MY GENERATION   The Who.....................
6 THE RIVER   Ken Dodd.................

I Saw Her Standing There

          E   A7   E
Well, she was just seventeen, you know what I mean,
     E7   B7
And the way she looked was way beyond compare,
     E   A7   Am   E   B7   E
So how could I dance with another, oh when I saw her standing there

Well she looked at me, and I, I could see, that before too long I'd fall
in love with her,
She wouldn't dance with another, oh when I saw her dancing there.
     A7
Well my heart went boom when I crossed the that room, and I held her hand in mine.

Oh we danced through the night, and we held each other tight, and before too long I fell in love with her,
Now I'll never dance with another, oh when I saw her standing there.

Well my heart went boom when I crossed that room, and I held her hand in mine.

Oh we danced through the night, and we held each other tight, and before too long I fell in love with her,
Now I'll never dance with another, oh since I saw her standing there. oh since I saw her standing there.
                                                              B7   A7

A Hard Day's Night

          G   D   G   F   G
It's been a hard day's night, and I've been working like a dog,
          G   D   G   F   G
It's been a hard day's night, I should be sleeping like a log,
          C   D7
But when I get home to you, I find the things that you do,
          G C7 G
Will make me feel al-right.

You know I work all day, to get you money to buy you things,
And it's worth it just to hear you say, you're gonna give me
ev'rything,
So why I love to come home, 'cause when I get you alone,
You know I feel okay.

          Bm Em   Bm
When I'm home ev'rything seems to be alright,
          G Em   C7   D7
When I'm home feeling you holding me tight, tight, yeh.

It's been a hard day's night, and I've been working like a dog,
It's been a hard day's night, I should be sleeping like a log,
But when I get home to you, I find the things that you do,
Will make me feel alright.

So why I love to come home, 'cause when I get you alone,
You know I feel okay.
When I'm home ev'rything seems to be alright,
When I'm home feeling you holding me tight, tight, yeh.

It's been a hard day's night, and I've been working like a dog,
It's been a hard day's night, I should be sleeping like a log,
But when I get home to you, I find the things that you do,
Will make me feel alright.

A: 'I Saw Her Standing There';
'Misery'; 'Anna (Go To Him)'; 'Chains'; 'Boys';
'Ask Me Why'; 'Please Please Me'.

B: 'Love Me Do'; 'PS I Love You'; 'Baby It's You';
'Do You Want To Know A Secret'; 'A Taste Of
Honey'; 'There's A Place'; 'Twist And Shout.

Please Please Me,
22 March 1963,
Parlophone PMC 1202
(mono), PCS 3042 (stereo).

She's A Woman

SINGLE: I Feel Fine/She's A Woman 27.11.1964

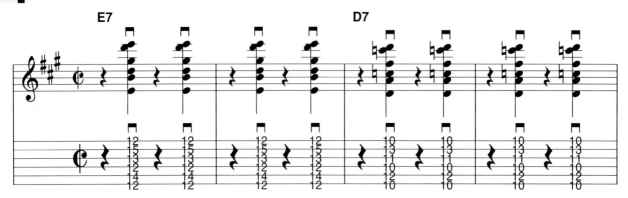

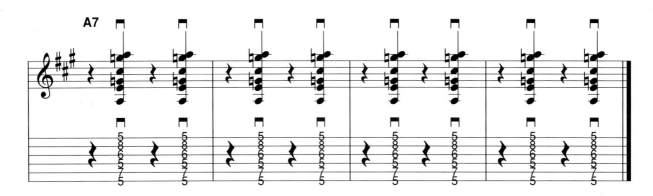

A	D7	A7

A   **D7**   **A7**
My love don't give me presents.

         D7   **A7**
I know that she's no peasant,

D7 Am7 D7   **D7**   **Am7 D7**
Only ever has to give me love forever and forever,

A   **D7**   **A7**
My love don't give me presents,

E7   **Bm7**   **E7**
Turn me on when I get lonely,

D7   **Am7 D7**   **A**   **D7**   **A7 E7**
People tell me that she's only foolin', I know she isn't.

         D7   **A7**
She don't give boys the eye,

         D7   **A7**
She hates to see me cry,

D7   **Am7 D7**   **Am7**   **D7**
She is happy just to hear me say that I will never leave her.

A   **D7**   **A7**
She don't give boys the eye,

E7   **Bm7**   **E7**
She will never make me jealous,

D7   **Am7**   **D7**   **A**   **D7**   **A7**
Gives me all her time as well as lovin', don't ask me why.

C#m   **F#7**
She's a woman who understands.

C#m   **Bm7**   **E7**
She's a woman who loves her man.

My love don't give me presents,
I know that she's no peasant,
Only ever has to give love forever and forever,
My love don't give me presents,
Turn me on when I get lonely,
People tell me that she's only foolin',
I know she isn't.

She's a woman who understands.
She's a woman who loves her man.

She don't give boys the eye,
She hates to see me cry,
She is happy just to hear me
Say that I will never leave her.
She don't give boys the eye,
She will never make me jealous,
Gives me all her time as well as lovin',
Don't ask me why.

She's a woman, she's a woman.

Michelle

ALBUM: Rubber Soul 3.12.1965

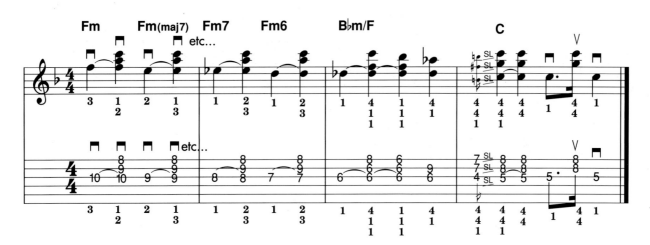

F   B♭m7
Michelle,   ma belle,

E♭   D♭   C D♭   C
These are words that go together well, my Michelle,

F   B♭m7
Michelle,   ma belle,

E♭   D♭   C
Sont les mots qui vont très bien ensemble,

D♭   C
Très bien ensemble.

Fm   E♭m
I love you, I love you, I love you,

A♭ D♭
That's all I want to say,

C   Fm B♭m   Fm   E+ Fm7
  Until I find a way, I will say the only words

Fm6   B♭m7   C
I know that you'll understand.

Michelle ma belle,
Sont les mots qui vont très bien ensemble,
Très bien ensemble.
I need to, I need to, I need to, I need to make you see,
Oh what you mean to me,
Until I do I'm hoping you will know what I mean.

I love you.
I want you, I want you, I want you,
I think you know by now,
I'll get to you some how,
Until I do I'm telling you so you'll understand.

Michelle ma belle,
Sont les mots qui vont très bien ensemble
Très bien ensemble.

D♭   Fm   B♭m   C
I will say the only words I know that you'll understand,

F   B♭m F
My Michelle.

6 Eight Days A Week

ALBUM: Beatles for Sale 4.12.1964

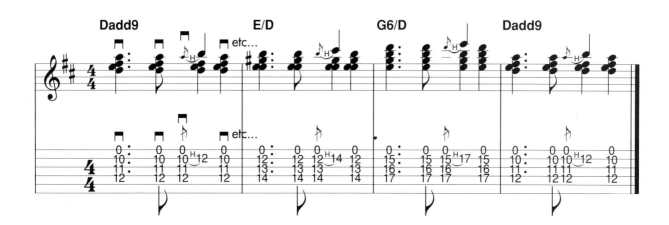

Dadd9   **E/D**   **G6/D**   **Dadd9**

```
D              E7        G              D
Ooh I need your love babe, guess you know it's true,
               E7        G         D
Hope you need my love babe just like I need you,
Bm    G       Bm     E7
Hold me, love me, hold me, love me,
 D             E7       G        D
Ain't got nothin' but love babe,   eight days a week.

Love you ev'ry day girl, always on my mind,
One thing I can say girl, love you all the time,
Hold me, love me, hold me, love me,
Ain't got nothin' but love babe, eight days a week.
 A             Bm
Eight days a week I love you,
 E7          G         A7
Eight days a week is not enough to show I care.

Ooh I need your love babe, guess you know it's true,
Hope you need my love babe just like I need you,
Hold me, love me, hold me, love me,
Ain't got nothin' but love babe, eight days a week.
Eight days a week I love you,
Eight days a week is not enough to show I care.

Love you ev'ry day girl, always on my mind,
One thing I can say girl, love you all the time,
Hold me, love me, hold me, love me,
Ain't got nothin' but love babe, eight days a week.
Eight days a week.  Eight days a week.
```

THE CHARTS   10 DECEMBER 1964
1 I FEEL FINE The Beatles...........
2 I'M GONNA BE STRONG Gene Pitney...........
3 LITTLE RED ROOSTER The Rolling Stones...........
4 DOWNTOWN Petula Clark...........
5 WALK TALL Val Doonican...........
6 THERE'S A HEARTACHE FOLLOWING ME
      Jim Reeves...........
7 ALL DAY AND ALL OF THE NIGHT The
      Kinks ....
8 BABY LOVE The Supremes...........
9 PRETTY PAPER Roy Orbison...........
10 UM UM UM UM UM UM Wayne Fontana and
      the Mindbenders...........

I Feel Fine

SINGLE: I Feel Fine/She's A Woman 27.11.1964

C7
Baby's good to me, you know,

She's happy as can be, you know, she said so. **G7**

G7   **F7**   **C**
I'm in love with her   and I feel fine.
Baby says she's mine you know,
She tells me all the time you know, she said so.
I'm in love with her and I feel fine.

C   **Em**   **F**
I'm so glad that she's my little girl,

G7 C   **Em**   **F**   **G7**
She's so glad she's telling all the world.

That her baby buys her things you know,
He buys her diamond rings you know, she said so.
She's in love with me and I feel fine.
Baby says she's mine you know,
She tells me all the time you know, she said so.
I'm in love with her and I feel fine.

I'm so glad that she's my little girl,
She's so glad she's telling all the world.
That her baby buys her things you know,
He buys her diamond rings you know, she said so.
She's in love with me and I feel fine.

8

I'll Follow The Sun

ALBUM: Beatles for Sale 4.12.1964

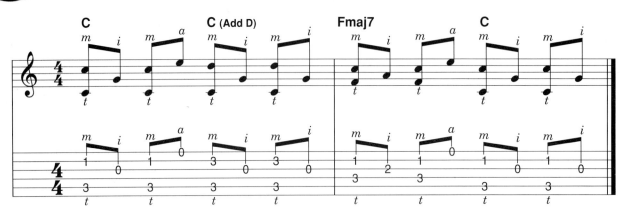

9

If I Needed Someone

ALBUM: Rubber Soul 3.12.1965

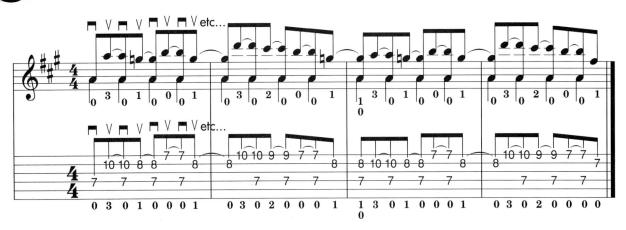

10

Revolution

SINGLE: Hey Jude/Revolution 30.5.1965
ALBUM: The Beatles 22.11.1965

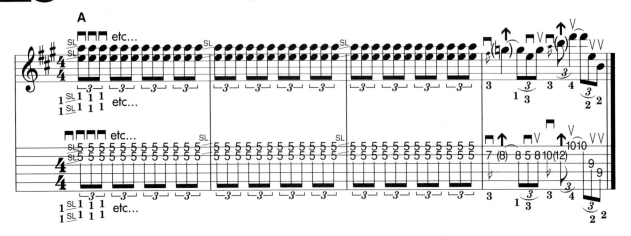

I'll Follow The Sun

G   F7   C   D7
One day you'll look to see I've gone,
             C7   Em D7 G7   C F C
For tomorrow may rain   so   I'll follow the sun.
Some day you'll know I was the one,
But tomorrow may rain so I'll follow the sun.
                   F   Fm   C
And now the time has come and so my love I must go,
               F   Fm   C   F
And though I lose a friend in the end you will know, oh

One day you'll look to see I've gone,
But tomorrow may rain so I'll follow the sun.
And now the time has come and so my love I must go,
And though I lose a friend in the end you will know, oh
One day you'll look to see I've gone,
For tomorrow may rain so I'll follow the sun.

If I Needed Someone

D   G
If I needed someone to love
D   G   C
You're the one that I'd be thinking of
Am7   D7   C D C
If I needed someone.
D   G
If I had some more time to spend
D   G   C
Then I guess I'd be with you my friend
Am7   D7   C D
If I needed someone.
Am   B7
Had you come some other day
                Em
Then it might not have been like this
Am   B7   Em A7
But you see now I'm too much in love
D   G
Carve your number on my wall
        D   G   C
And maybe you will get a call from me
Am7   D7   C D C D C D C D C D C D C D
If I needed someone.

Had you come some other day
Then it might not have been like this
But you see now I'm too much in love
Carve your number on my wall
And maybe you will get a call from me
If I needed someone ah ah.

Revolution

             A
You say you want a revolution
               D   A
Well, you know we all want to change the world.
      A
You tell me that it's revolution,
               D   E7
Well, you know we all want to change the world.
B   D
  But when you talk about destruction,
B   F#7
  Don't you know that you can count me out.
D   A   D   A
  Don't you know it's going to be alright,
     D A D A
Alright, alright,   alright.

You say you got a real solution
Well, you know we'd all love to see the plan.
You ask me for a contribution,
Well, you know we're doing what we can.
But if you want money for people with minds that hate,
All I can tell you is brother you have to wait.
Don't you know it's going to be alright,
Alright, alright, alright.

You say you'll change a constitution
Well, you know we all want to change your head.
You tell me it's the institution,
Well, you know you better free your mind instead.
But if you go carrying pictures of Chairman Mao,
You ain't going to make it with anyone anyhow.
Don't you know it's going to be alright,
Alright, alright, alright.

THE CHARTS   11 SEPTEMBER 1968
1 HEY JUDE The Beatles.............
2 I'VE GOTTA GET A MESSAGE TO YOU The Bee Gees
3 DO IT AGAIN The Beach Boys.............
4 I SAY A LITTLE PRAYER Aretha Franklin.............
5 HOLD ME TIGHT Johnny Nash.............
6 THIS GUY'S IN LOVE WITH YOU Herb Alpert.............
7 THOSE WERE THE DAYS Mary Hopkin.............
8 HELP YOURSELF Tom Jones.............
9 HIGH IN THE SKY Amen Corner.............
10 ON THE ROAD AGAIN Canned Heat.............

Revolution was the B Side of Hey Jude

11 Act Naturally

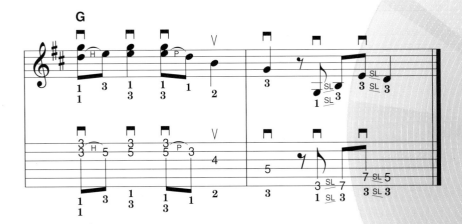

Help!, 6 August 1965, Parlophone PMC
1255 (mono, PCS 3071 (stereo)).

A: 'Help!'; 'The Night Before'; 'You've Got To Hide
Your Love Away'; 'I Need You'; 'Another Girl';
'You're Going To Lose That Girl'; 'Ticket to Ride'.

B: 'Act Naturally'; 'It's Only Love'; 'You Like Me Too
Much'; 'Tell Me What You See'; 'I've Just Seen A
Face'; 'Yesterday'; 'Dizzy Miss Lizzy'.

D   **G**
They're gonna put me in the movies,
D   **A7**
They're gonna make a big star out of me,
     D   **G**
We'll make a film about a man that's sad and lonely
  A7   **G**
and all I gotta do is act naturally,
    A7   **D**
Well I'll bet you I'm gonna be a big star,
    A7   **D**
Might win an Oscar you can't never tell,
   A7   **D**
The movies gonna make me a big star,
    E7   **A7**
'Cause I can play the part so well,

Hope you come and see me in the movies,
Then I know that you will plainly see,
The biggest fool that ever hit the big time,
and all I gotta do is act naturally,
Make the scene about a man that's sad and lonely
and beggin' down upon his bended knee,
I'll play the part but I won't need rehearsin'
all I have to do is act naturally;

Well I'll bet you I'm gonna be a big star,
Might win an Oscar you can't never tell,
The movies gonna make me a big star,
'Cause I can play the part so well.

Hope you come and see me in the movies,
Then I know that you will plainly see,
The biggest fool that ever hit the big time,
And all I gotta do is act naturally.

12 Ticket To Ride

SINGLE: Ticket To Ride/Yes It Is 9.4.1965

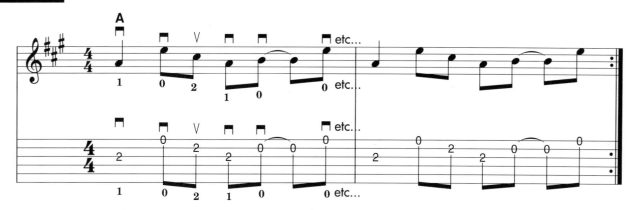

E
I think I'm gonna be sad, I think it's today, yeh,
                               F♯m7   **B7**
The girl that's driving me mad, is going away.
C♯m   **A**
She's got a ticket to ride,
C♯m   **D**
She's got a ticket to ri - hi - hide,
C♯m   **B7**   **E**
She's got a ticket to ride, but she don't care.

She said that living with me, is bringing her down yeh,
For she would never be free, when I was around.
She's got a ticket to ride,
She's got a ticket to ri - hi - hide,
She's got a ticket to ride, but she don't care.

 A7
I don't know why she's riding so high,
She ought to think right,
                       B
She ought to do right by me.
 A7
Before she gets to saying goodbye,
She ought to think right,
                       B
She ought to do right by me.

I think I'm gonna be sad, I think it's today yeh,
The girl that's driving me mad, is going away.
She's got a ticket to ride,
She's got a ticket to ri - hi - hide,
She's got a ticket to ride, but she don't care.

I don't know why she's riding so high,
She ought to think right,
She ought to do right by me,
Before she gets to saying goodbye,
She ought to think right,
She ought to do right by me.

She said that living with me, is bringing her down yeh,
For she would never be free, when I was around.
She's got a ticket to ride,
She's got a ticket to ri - hi - hide,
She's got a ticket to ride, but she don't care.

                   E
My baby don't care.
                   E
My baby don't care.
                   E
My baby don't care.

THE CHARTS   22 APRIL 1965
1 TICKET TO RIDE The Beatles ....
2 HERE COMES THE NIGHT Them ....
3 THE MINUTE YOU'RE GONE Cliff Richard ....
4 CONCRETE AND CLAY Unit Four Plus Two.....
5 LITTLE THINGS Dave Berry ....
6 CATCH THE WIND Donovan ....
7 FOR YOUR LOVE The Yardbirds ....
8 KING OF THE ROAD Roger Miller............
9 THE LAST TIME The Rolling Stones ....
10 POP FOR THE WORKERS The Barron Knights ....

Rain

SINGLE: Paperback Writer/Rain 10.6.1966

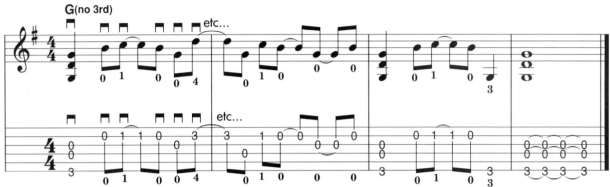

    G   C   D   G
If the rain comes they run and hide their heads.
    C   D   G
They might as well be dead,
    C   G
If the rain comes, if the rain comes.

When the sun shines they slip into the shade,
And sip their lemonade,
When the sun shines, when the sun shines.

  G C   G
Rain,   I don't mind,
       C   G
Shine,   the weather's fine.
                 C   D   G
I can show you that when it starts to rain,
C   D   G
Everything's the same,
        C   G
I can show you, I can show you.

Rain, I don't mind,
Shine, the weather's fine.
Can you hear me when it rains and shines,
It's just a state of mind,
Can you hear me, can you hear me?

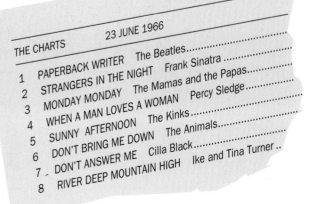

THE CHARTS   23 JUNE 1966

1 PAPERBACK WRITER   The Beatles.............
2 STRANGERS IN THE NIGHT   Frank Sinatra.............
3 MONDAY MONDAY   The Mamas and the Papas............
4 WHEN A MAN LOVES A WOMAN   Percy Sledge.............
5 SUNNY AFTERNOON   The Kinks.............
6 DON'T BRING ME DOWN   The Animals.............
7 DON'T ANSWER ME   Cilla Black.............
8 RIVER DEEP MOUNTAIN HIGH   Ike and Tina Turner.

14 Honey Don't

ALBUM: Beatles For Sale 4.12.1964

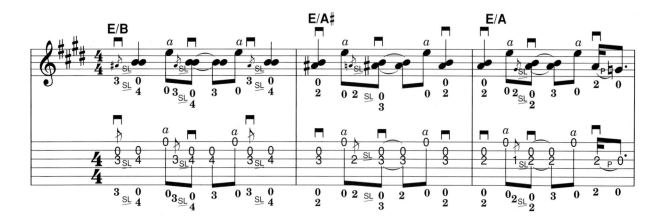

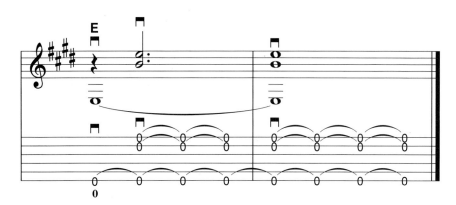

E
Well, how come you say you will when you won't

C
Say you do, baby when you don't,

E
Let me know honey, how you feel.

C   **B**
Tell the truth now, is love real? So aw, aw,

B7   **E**
   Well, honey, don't. Well, honey don't,

                  A7   **E**
Honey don't, honey don't,   honey don't,

        B7
I say you will when you won't,

                 E
Aw, aw, honey don't.

Well I love you, baby, and you ought to know
I like the way that you wear your clothes,
Everything about you is so dog-gone sweet,
You got that sand all over your feet, so aw, aw,
Well, honey, don't. Honey don't,
Honey don't, honey don't, honey don't,
I say you will when you won't,
Aw, aw, honey don't.

Sometimes I love you on a Saturday night,
Sunday morning you don't look right,
You been out painting the town,
Uh - huh, baby you been slipping around so aw, aw,
Well, honey, don't, I say honey don't,
Honey don't, honey don't, honey don't,
I say you will when you won't,
Aw, aw, honey don't,
I feel fine oo oo I say.

E
   Well, honey don't,

          A7
Well, honey don't,

                 E
A little, little, honey don't,

          B7
I say you will when you won't,

               E
Aw, aw, honey don't.

I Don't Want To Spoil The Party

ALBUM: Beatles For Sale 4.12.1964

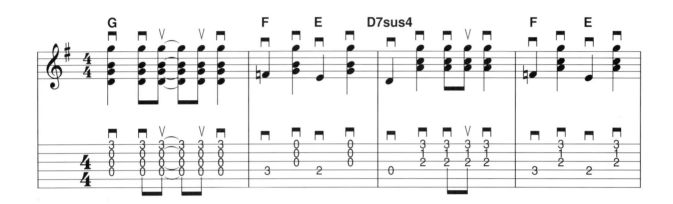

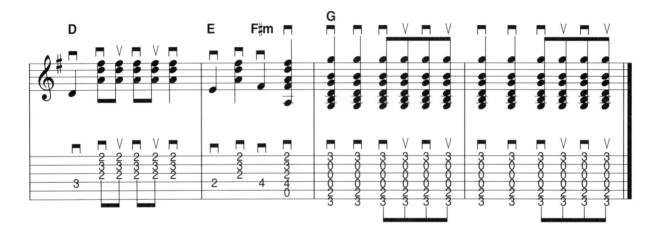

Em7 A7   D   G   D   E7 A7
I   don't want to spoil the par - ty   so I'll go,

Em7 A7   D   G   D   A7
I   would hate my disappoint - ment to show,

        Bm   F7 Em7   A7
There's nothing for me here   so I will disappear,

Em7 A7 D   C   D
If   she turns up while I'm gone   please let me know.

I've had a drink or two and I don't care,
There's no fun in what I do if she's not there,
I wonder what went wrong I've waited far too long,
I think I'll take a walk and look for her.

Em7   A7   D   Bm E7 G A7
Though tonight she's made me sad, I   still love her.

Em7 A7   D   Bm E7 G A7
If   I find   her I'll be glad, I   still love her.

I don't want to spoil the party so I'll go,
I would hate my disappointment to show,
There's nothing for me here so I will disappear,
If she turns up while I'm gone please let me know.

Though tonight she's made me sad, I still love her.
If I find her I'll be glad, I still love her.

I've had a drink or two and I don't care,
There's no fun in what I do if she's not there,
I wonder what went wrong I've waited far too long,
I think I'll take a walk and look for her.

Dear Prudence

ALBUM: The Beatles 22.11.1965

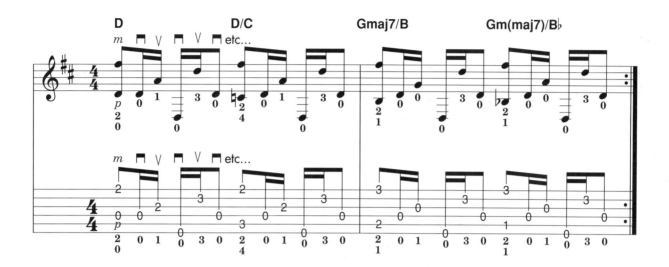

      G   G7 C Cm   G   G7 C Cm
Dear Prudence,   won't you come out to play?
      G   G7 C Cm   G   G7 C Cm
Dear Prudence,   greet the brand new day.
      G   G7   C   Cm
The sun is up, the sky is blue. It's beautiful and so are you.
      G   G7 F   C   G   G7 C Cm
Dear Prudence   won't you come out to play?

Dear Prudence open up your eyes.
Dear Prudence see the sunny skies.
The wind is low the birds will sing that you are part of everything.
                                 G   C D C
Dear Prudence won't you open up your eyes?

      G   C
Look around round
      G   C
Look around round round
        B♭   C   G G7 C Cm
Look around.

Dear Prudence let me see your smile.
Dear Prudence like a little child.
The clouds will be a daisy chain. So let me see you smile again.
Dear Prudence won't you let me see you smile?

Dear Prudence, won't you come out to play.
Dear Prudence, greet the brand new day.
The sun is up, the sky is blue. It's beautiful and so are you.
Dear Prudence won't you come out to play?

17

From Me To You

SINGLE: From Me To You/Thank You Girl 11.4.1963

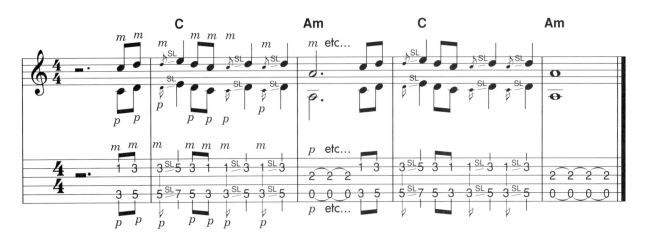

18

Don't Let Me Down

SINGLE: Get Back/Don't Let Me Down 11.4.1969

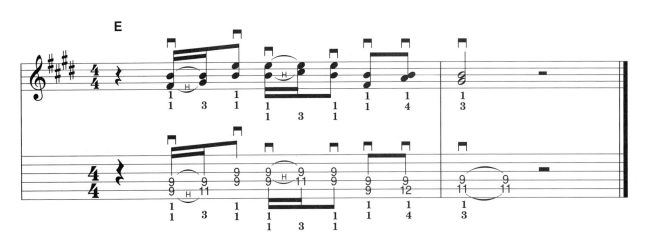

19

This Boy

SINGLE: I Want To Hold Your Hand/This Boy 29.11.1963

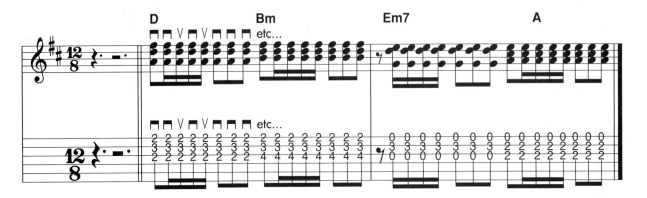

From Me To You

```
        C              Am
If there's anything that you want,
        C              G7
If there's anything I can do,
  F7              Am
Just call on me and I'll send it along,
        C     G7        C  Am
With love  from me    to you.
```

I've got ev'rything that you want,
Like a heart that's oh so true,
Just call on me and I'll send it along,
With love from me to you.

```
   Gm7              C7
I got arms that long to hold you,
   F     C7      F
And keep you by my side,
   Am              C7
I got lips that long to kiss you,
  G7           G7+
And keep you satisfied.
```

If there's anything
that you want,
If there's anything I
can do,
Just call on me and I'll send it along,
With love from me to you.

I got arms that long to hold you,
And keep you by my side,
I got lips that long to kiss you,
And keep you satisfied.

If there's anything that you want,
If there's anything I can do,
Just call on me and I'll send it along,
With love from me to you.

This Boy

```
  D    Bm Em      A7   D  Bm Em
That boy        took my love away,
      A7      D  Bm
He'll regret it someday,
  G     A7          D   Bm Em A7
But this boy wants you back again.
  D    Bm Em    A7     D  Bm Em
That boy        isn't good for you,
          A7     D  Bm
Though he may want you too,
  G     A7          D   Bm Em A7
This boy wants you back again.
```

```
D7    G            F#m7
Oh, and this boy would be happy,
    Bm           D7
Just to love you, but oh my - yi - yi,
G              E7
That boy won't be happy,
A7
Till he's seen you cry - hi - hi.
```

This boy wouldn't mind the pain,
Would always feel the same,
If this boy gets you back again.
```
   D     Bm Em A7 D     Bm Em A7
This boy.            This boy.
```

Don't Let Me Down

```
          F#m7              E
Don't let me down, don't let me down.
          F#m7              E
Don't let me down, don't let me down.
```

```
E                        F#m7
Nobody ever loved me like she does,
            E
Ooh she does. Yes she does,
                        F#m7
And if somebody loved me Like she do me,
            E
Ooh she do me. Yes she does.
```

Don't let me down, don't let me down.
Don't let me down, don't let me down.

And from the first time that she really done me,
Ooh she done me. She done me good,
I guess nobody ever really done me,
Ooh she done me. She done me good.

```
              E
I'm in love for the first time,
                    B
Don't you know it's going to last,
                 B7
It's a love that lasts forever,
              E
It's a love that has no past.
```

Don't let me down, don't let me down.
Don't let me down, don't let me down.

19

20 Sgt. Pepper's Lonely Hearts Club Band

ALBUM: Sgt. Pepper 1.6.1967

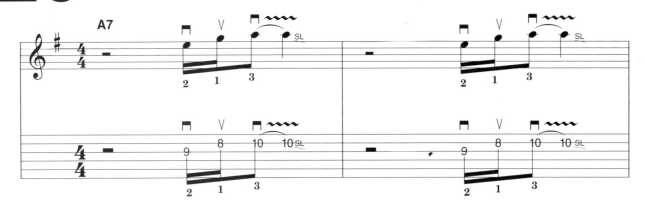

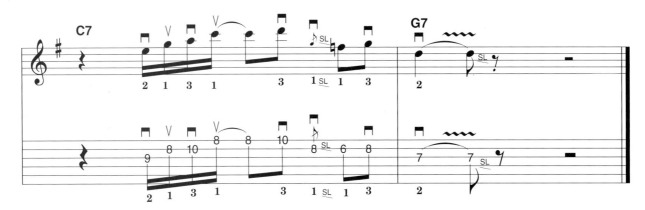

It was twenty years ago today,
Sgt. Pepper taught the band to play,
They've been going in and out of style,
But they're guaranteed to raise a smile.
So may I introduce to you
The act you've known for all these years,
Sgt. Pepper's Lonely Hearts Club Band.

I don't really want to stop the show,
But I thought you might like to know,
That the singer's going to sing a song,
And he wants you all to sing along.
So may I introduce to you
The one and only Billy Shears
And Sgt. Pepper's Lonely
Hearts Club Band.

      A   **C6 Bm7 Am7 D7   A**
We're Sgt. Pepper's Lone-ly   Hearts Club Band,
  D7   **A**
We hope you will enjoy the show,
      A   **C6 Bm7 Am7 D7   A**
We're Sgt. Pepper's Lonely Hearts Club Band,
  B7   **E7**
Sit back and let the evening go.
 D   **A**
Sgt. Pepper's Lonely, Sgt. Pepper's Lonely,
B7   **D7**   **A**
Sgt. Pepper's Lonely Hearts Club Band.

   D7   **G7**
It's wonderful to be here, it's certainly a thrill.
    D7
You're such a lovely audience,
    E7
We'd like to take you home with us,
We'd love to take you home.

Sgt Pepper's Lonely Hearts
Club Band, 1 June 1967,
Parlophone PMC 7027
(mono), PCS 7027 (stereo).

A: 'Sgt Pepper's Lonely Hearts Club Band'; 'With A Little Help From My Friends'; 'Lucy In The Sky With Diamonds'; 'Getting Better'; 'Fixing A Hole'; 'She's Leaving Home'; 'Being For The Benefit Of Mr Kite!'.

B: 'Within You Without You'; 'When I'm Sixty-Four'; 'Lovely Rita'; 'Good Morning Good Morning'; 'Sgt. Pepper's Lonely Hearts Club Band (Reprise)'; 'A Day In The Life'.

21 Across The Universe

ALBUM: Let It Be 8.5.1970

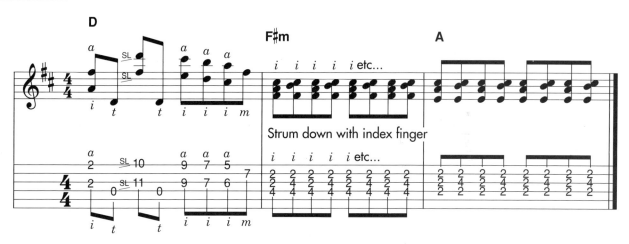

Strum down with index finger

A   **F#m7**   **C#m**
Words are flying out like endless rain into a paper cup,

   Bm7   **E7**
They slither while they pass, they slip away across the universe.

A   **F#m7**   **C#m**
Pools of sorrow, waves of joy are drifting through my open mind,

Bm7   **Dm**
Possessing and caressing me.

A   **E7**
Jai Guru De Va Om
Nothing's gonna change my world,

   D   **A**
Nothing's gonna change my world.

Images of broken light which dance before me like a million eyes,
That call me on and on across the universe,
Thoughts meander like a restless wind
Inside a letter box they
Tumble blindly as they make their way
Across the universe.
Jai Guru De Va Om

   D
Nothing's gonna change my world,

              A
Nothing's gonna change my world.

Sounds of laughter shades of earth are ringing
Through my open views inciting and inviting me.
Limitless undying love which shines around me like a million suns,
It calls me on and on across the universe.

   A   **E7**
Jai Guru De Va Om
Nothing's gonna change my world,

   D   **A**
Nothing's gonna change my world.

22 I Want To Hold Your Hand

SINGLE: I Want To Hold Your Hand/This Boy 29.11.1963

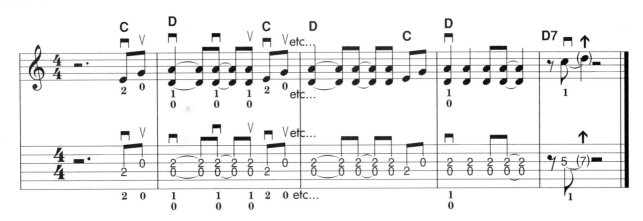

23 You Can't Do That

SINGLE: Can't Buy Me Love/You Can't Do That 20.3.1964

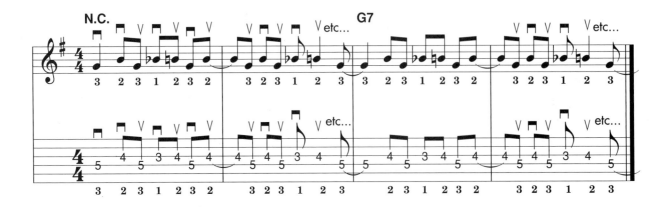

I Want To Hold Your Hand

A7 D   A7
Oh yeh, I'll tell you something,
Bm   Fm
I think you'll understand,
D   A7
When I'll say that something,
Bm   Fm
I wanna hold your hand,
G   A7   D   Bm
I wanna hold your hand,
G   A7   D
I wanna hold your hand.

Oh please say to me
You'll let me be your man,
And please say to me
You'll let me hold your hand,
Now let me hold your hand,
I wanna hold your hand.

Am7   D7   G   Em
And when I touch you I feel happy inside,
Am7   D7   G   A7
It's such a feeling that my love I can't hide,
G   A7
I can't hide, I can't hide.

Yeh, you got that something,
I think you'll understand,
When I feel that something,
I wanna hold your hand,
I wanna hold your hand,
I wanna hold your hand.

And when I touch you I feel happy inside,
It's such a feeling that my love I can't hide,
I can't hide, I can't hide.
I wanna hold your hand,
I wanna hold your hand.

You Can't Do That

     G7   Dm7   G7
I got something to say that might cause you pain,
         Dm7   G7
If I catch you talking to that boy again,
        C7   G
I'm gonna let you down, and leave you flat,
        D7   C7   G
Because I told you before, oh, you can't do that.

Well, it's the second time, I've caught you talking to him,
Do I have to tell you one more time,
I think it's a sin, I think I'll let you down,
Because I've told you before, oh, you can't do that.

G   B7 Em
  Ev'rybody's green,
         Am   D7   G
'Cause I'm the one, who won your love,
         B7 Em   Am
But if they'd seen,   you talking that way
      D7
They'd laugh in my face.

So please listen to me, if you wanna stay mine,
I can't help my feeling, I'll go out of my mind,
You know I'll let you down,
And leave you flat,
Because I've told you before, oh,
You can't do that.

Ev'rybody's green,
'Cause I'm the one, who won your love,
But if they'd seen, you talking that way
They'd laugh in my face.

So please listen to me, if you wanna stay mine,
I can't help my feeling, I'll go out of my mind,
I know I'll let you down,
And leave you flat,
Because I've told you before, oh,
You can't do that.

In My Life

ALBUM: Rubber Soul 3.12.1965

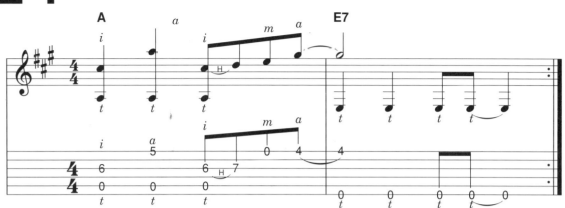

In My Life

       A   **Fm**   **A7**
There are places I'll remember
D Dm   **A**
All my life,   though some have changed,
                  Fm
Some forever, not for better,
         D Dm   **A**
Some have gone   and some remain.
         Fm   **D**
All these places have their moments,
     G   **A**
With lovers and friends I still can recall,
       Fm   **B7**
Some are dead and some are living,
   D Dm   **A**   **E**
In my life I've loved them all.

But of all these friends and lovers,
There is no one compares with you,
And these memories lose their meaning
When I think of love as something new.
Though I know I'll never lose affection
For people and things that went before,
Though I know I'll often stop and think about them,
In my life I'll love you more.

Though I know I'll never lose affection
For people and things that went before,
I know I'll often stop and think about them
In my life I'll love you more.
In my life I'll love you more.

THE CHARTS
2 DECEMBER 1965
1 THE CARNIVAL IS OVER The Seekers
2 MY GENERATION The Who
3 1-2-3 Len Barry
4 GET OFF OF MY CLOUD The Rolling Stones
5 A LOVER'S CONCERTO The Toys
6 TEARS Ken Dodd
7 WIND ME UP (LET ME GO) Cliff Richard
8 POSITIVELY 4TH STREET Bob Dylan
9 PRINCESS IN RAGS Gene Pitney
10 YESTERDAY MAN Chris Andrews

Two Of Us
ALBUM: Let It Be 8.5.1970

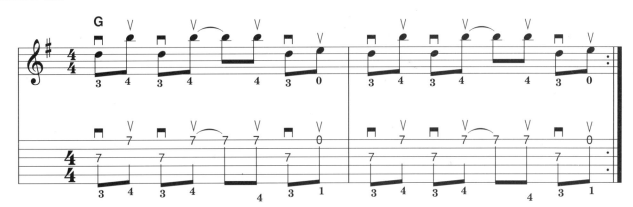

G
Two of us riding nowhere

          C G   Am
Spending someone's hard earned pay.

G
You and me Sunday driving,

          C G Am   G C D
Not arriving on our way back home.

            G   C
We're on our way home,

D   **G**
We're on our way home,

C   **G**
We're going home.

Two of us sending postcards
Writing letters on my wall.
You and me burning matches,
Lifting latches on our way back home.
We're on our way home,
We're on our way home,
We're going home.

B♭   **Dm**
You and I have memories

Gm   **Am7**   **Am**
Longer than the road that stretches out ahead.

Two of us wearing raincoats
Standing solo in the sun.
You and me chasing paper,
Getting nowhere on our way back home.
We're on our way home,
We're on our way home,
We're going home.

Two of us wearing raincoats
Standing solo in the sun.
You and me chasing paper,
Getting nowhere on our way back home.
We're on our way home,
We're on our way home,
We're going home.
We're going home.

THE CHARTS   9 MAY 1970
1   SPIRIT IN THE SKY   Norman Greenbaum.............
2   BACK HOME   England World Cup Squad ....
3   ALL KINDS OF EVERYTHING   Dana ....
4   BRIDGE OVER TROUBLED WATER   Simon and Garfun..
5   DAUGHTER OF DARKNESS   Tom Jones ....
6   HOUSE OF THE RISING SUN   Frijid Pink.........
7   CAN'T HELP FALLING IN LOVE   Andy Williams......
8   TRAVELLIN' BAND   Creedence Clearwater Reviva
9   NEVER HAD A DREAM COME TRUE   Steveie

26

And I Love Her

ALBUM: A Hard Day's Night 10.7.1964

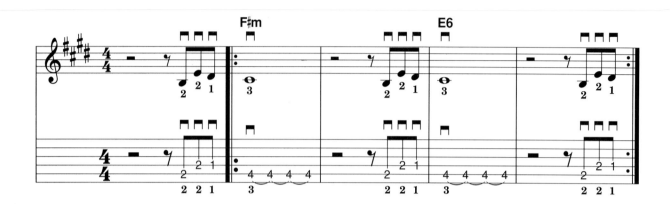

27

It's Only Love

ALBUM: Help 6.5.1965

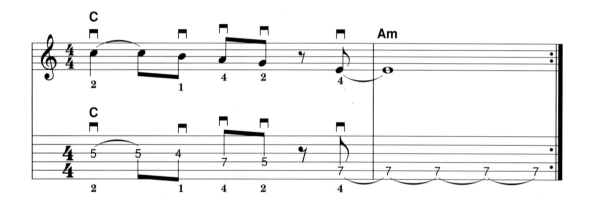

28

What You're Doing

ALBUM: Beatles For Sale 4.12.1964

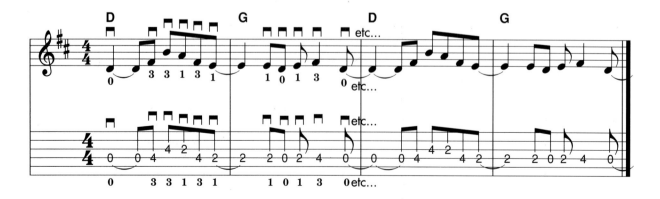

And I Love Her

F#m   C#m   F#m   C#m
I give her all my love,   that's all I do,
F#m   C#m   A   B   E
And if you saw my love, you'd love her too. I love her.

She gives me ev'rything, and tenderly,
The kiss my lover brings, she brings to me, and I love her.

C#m   G#m C#m   G#m
A love like ours,   could never die,
C#m   G#m   B
As long as I have you near me.

Bright are the stars that shine, dark is the sky,
I know this love of mine, will never die; and I love her.

Bright are the stars that shine, dark is the sky,
I know this love of mine, will never die, and I love her.

A: 'A Hard Day's Night'; 'I Should Have Known Better'; 'If I Fell'; 'I'm Happy Just To Dance With You'; 'And I Love Her'; 'Tell Me Why'; 'Can't Buy Me Love'.

B: 'Any Time At All'; 'I'll Cry Instead'; 'Things We Said Today'; 'When I Get Home'; 'You Can't Do That'; 'I'll Be Back'.

A Hard Day's Night, 10 July 1964,
Parlophone PMC 1230 (mono),
PCS 3058 (stereo).

It's Only Love

A   G   D   Bm7   E7 E+
I get high when I see you go by,
My oh my,
A   G   D   Bm7   E7 E+
When you sigh, my, my inside just flies,
Butterflies,
D   E7   A   F#m
Why am I so shy when I'm beside you?
     G   E7
It's only love and that is all,
     A   F#m
Why should I feel the way I do?
     G   E7
It's only love and that is all,
       D   E7
But it's so hard loving you.

Is it right that you and I should fight
Every night?
Just the sight of you makes night time bright,
Very bright.
Haven't I the right to make it up, girl?
It's only love and that is all,
Why should I feel the way I do?
It's only love and that is all,
But it's so hard loving you.
      D   E7
Yes, it's so hard loving you,
     A F#m A F#m A
loving you.

What You're Doing

D   G7
Look what you're doing,
D   G7
I'm feeling blue and lonely,
         D   G7
Would it be too much to ask of you,
               D G7
What you're doing to me?

You got me running
And there's no fun in it,
Why should it be so much to ask of you,
What you're doing to me?

                    D   G7
I've been waiting here for you,
                  D   E7
Wond'ring what you're gonna do,
                         A7
Should you need a love that's true, it's me.

Please stop your lying,
You've got me crying, girl,
Why should it be so much to ask of you,
What you're doing to me?

I've been waiting here for you,
Wond'ring what you're gonna do,
Should you need a love that's true, it's me.
Please stop your lying, you've got me crying, girl,
Why should it be so much to ask of you,
What you're doing to me?
What you're doing to me.
What you're doing to me.

29 Octopus's Garden

ALBUM: Abbey Road 26.9.1969

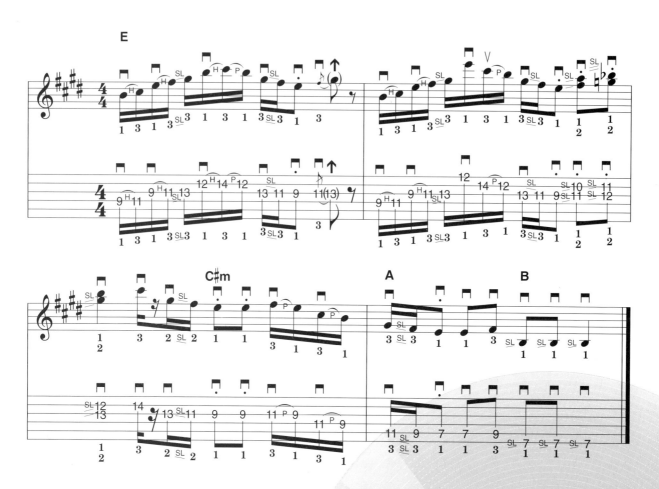

Abbey Road, 26 September 1969,
Apple [Parlophone] PMC 7088
(stereo only).

A: 'Come Together'; 'Something'; 'Maxwell's Silver Hammer'; 'Oh! Darling'; 'Octopus's Garden'; 'I Want You (She's So Heavy)'.

B: 'Here Comes The Sun'; 'Because'; 'You Never Give Me Your Money'; 'Sun King'/'Mean Mr Mustard'; 'Polythene Pam'/'She Came In Through The Bathroom Window'; 'Golden Slumbers'/ 'Carry That Weight'; 'The End'; 'Her Majesty'.

E♯   C♯m   A   B
I'd like to be under the sea in an octopus's garden in the shade,
E♯   C♯m   A   B
He'd let us in, knows where we've been, in his octopus's garden in the shade.
C♯m   A   B
I'd ask my friends to come and see in an octopus's garden with me.
E♯   C♯m   A   B
I'd like to be under the sea in an octopus's garden in the shade.

We would be warm below the storm in our little hide-a-way beneath the waves.
Resting our head on the sea bed in an octopus's garden near a cave.
We would sing and dance around because we know we can't be found.
I'd like to be under the sea in an octopus's garden in the shade.
Ah ah ah ah ah ah ah ah.

We would shout and swim about the coral that lies beneath the waves,
Oh what joy for every girl and boy knowing they're happy and they're safe.
We would be so happy, you and me, no-one there to tell us what to do,
I'd like to be under the sea in an octopus's garden with you.
In an octopus's garden with you.
In an octopus's garden with you.

30 Norwegian Wood

ALBUM: Rubber Soul 3.12.1965

*CAPO on 2nd fret so that it shifts the key to E (same as original recording)

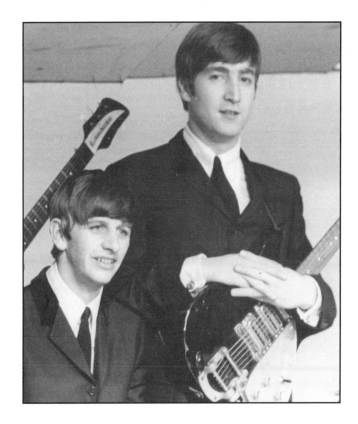

D   **C**   **D**
I once had a girl, or I should say she once had me.
                         C   **D**
She showed me her room, isn't it good? Norwegian wood.
Dm   **G**
She asked me to stay and she told me to sit anywhere,
 Dm   **G**   **A7**
So I looked around and I noticed there wasn't a chair.

I sat on a rug biding my time, drinking her wine.
We talked until two, and then she said, "It's time for bed".
She told me she worked in the morning and started to laugh,
I told her I didn't, and crawled off to sleep in the bath.

And when I awoke I was alone, this bird had flown,
So I lit a fire, isn't it good? Norwegian wood.

Doctor Robert

ALBUM: Revolver 5.8.1966

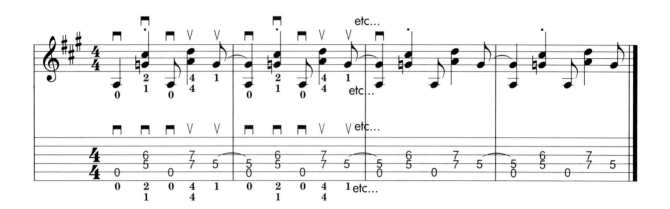

A   Em7 A   Em7   A   Em7 A Em7
Ring my friend I said you'd call Doctor Robert,

A   Em7   A   Em7 A Em7 A   F#7   C#m7 F#7
Day or night he'll be there anytime at all,   Doctor Robert, Doctor Robert.

          C#m7 F#7   C#m7 F#7
You're a new and better man, he helps you to understand,

          E   F#7   B
He does ev'rything he can, Doctor Robert.

If you're down he'll pick you up, Doctor Robert,
Take a drink from his special cup, Doctor Robert, Doctor Robert,
He's a man you must believe, helping ev'ry one in need,
No-one can succeed like Doctor Robert.

                        E   B
Well, well, well, you're feeling fine,

                        E   A   Em7 A
Well, well, well, he'll make you Doctor Robert.

My friend works with the National Health, Doctor Robert,
Don't pay money just to see yourself Doctor Robert,
Doctor Robert,
You're a new and better man, he helps you to understand,
He does ev'rything he can, Doctor Robert.

Well, well, well, you're feeling fine,
Well, well, well, he'll make you Doctor Robert.

Ring my friend I said you'd call, Doctor Robert.
Ring my friend I said you'd call, Doctor Robert,
Doctor Robert.

THE CHARTS   4 AUGUST 1966

1 WITH A GIRL LIKE YOU   The Troggs.................
2 OUT OF TIME   Chris Farlowe and the Thunderbird
3 BLACK IS BLACK   Los Bravos.......................
4 THE MORE I SEE YOU   Chris Montez.................
5 GET AWAY   Georgie Fame and the Blue Flames ...
6 LOVE LETTERS   Elvis Presley.....................
7 MAMA   Dave Berry ....
8 I COULDN'T LIVE WITHOUT YOUR LOVE   Petu'
9 SUNNY AFTERNOON   The Kinks.......
10 GOING BACK   Dusty Springfield.........

Run For Your Life

ALBUM: Rubber Soul 3.12.1965

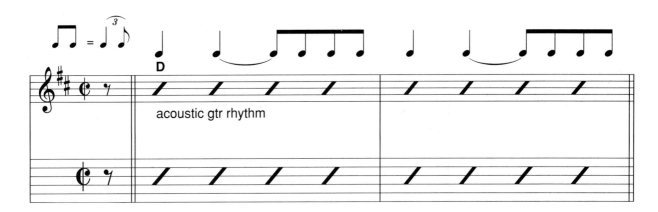

acoustic gtr rhythm

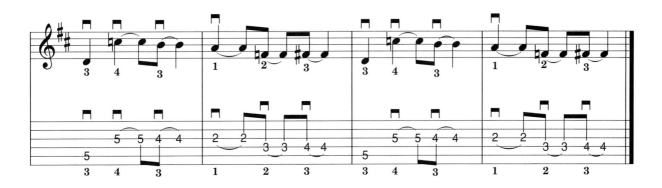

D
Well, I'd rather see you dead, little girl,
   Bm
Than to be with another man.
   D
You'd better keep your head, little girl,
   Bm
Or I won't know where I am.
                  E
You'd better run for your life if you can, little girl,
Bm   **E**
Hide your head in the sand, little girl.
Bm   **Em**
Catch you with another man,
F7   **Bm**
That's the end - ah, little girl.

Well you know that I'm a wicked guy
And I was born with a jealous mind,
And I can't spend my whole life tryin',
Just to make you toe the line.

You'd better run for your life if you can, little girl,
Hide your head in the sand, little girl,
Catch you with another man,
That's the end - ah, little girl.

Let this be a sermon,
I mean everything I said,
Baby, I'm determined,
And I'd rather see you dead.

You'd better run for your life if you can, little girl,
Hide your head in the sand, little girl,
Catch you with another man,
That's the end - ah, little girl,

I'd rather see you dead, little girl
Than to be with another man.
You'd better keep your head, little girl,
Or I won't know where I am.

You'd better run for your life if you can, little girl,
Hide your head in the sand, little girl,
Catch you with another man,
That's the end - ah, little girl.
Na na na, na na na, na na na.

33

Drive My Car
ALBUM: Rubber Soul 3.12.1965

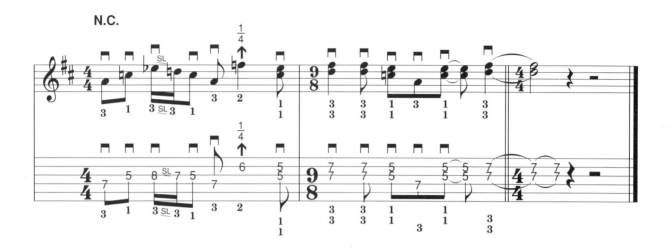

34

Dig A Pony
ALBUM: Let It Be 8.5.1970

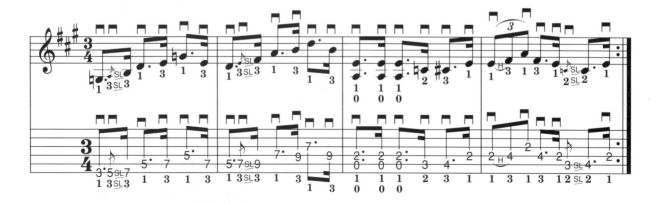

Drive My Car

Em7   D
      Asked a girl what she wanted to be,
Em7   D
      She said, "Baby can't you see?
Em7   D
      I wanna be famous, a star of the screen,
   Am7
But you can do something in between.
Em7   D7
Baby, you can drive my car,
Em7   D7
yes I'm gonna be a star,
Em7   D7
Baby, you can drive my car,
    A7   D7
and maybe I'll love you."

I told that girl that my prospects were good,
She said, "Baby it's understood,
Working for peanuts is all very fine,
But I can show you a better time",

"Baby, you can drive my car, yes I'm gonna be a star,
Baby, you can drive my car, and maybe I'll love you."
Beep beep mm, beep beep yeh!

"Baby, you can drive my car, yes I'm gonna be a star,
Baby, you can drive my car, and maybe I'll love you."

I told that girl I could start right away,
And she said, "Listen, babe, I've got something to say,
Got no car, and it's breaking my heart,
But I've found a driver, that's a start."

"Baby, you can drive my car, yes I'm gonna be a star,
Baby, you can drive my car, and maybe I'll love you."
Beep beep mm, beep beep yeh!
Beep beep mm, beep beep yeh!
Beep beep mm, beep beep yeh!

Dig A Pony

A D A D A   F#m
I hi hi hi hi hi hi hi dig a pony,
                  Bm   G
Well you can celebrate anything you want,
               Bm   G   E7
Yes you can celebrate anything you want ooh.

I hi hi hi hi hi hi hi do a road hog,
Well you can penetrate any place you go,
Yes you can penetrate any place you go.

               G   D   A
I told you so, all I want is you.
G   D   A E7
Everything has got to be just like you want it to. Because

I hi hi hi hi hi hi hi pick a moon dog,
Well you can radiate ev'rything you are,
Yes you can radiate ev'rything you are ooh.

I hi hi hi hi hi hi hi roll a stoney,
Well you can imitate ev'ryone you know,
Yes you can imitate ev'ryone you know.

I hi hi hi hi hi hi hi feel the wind blow,
Well you can indicate ev'rything you see,
Yes you can indicate ev'rything you see ooh.

I hi hi hi hi hi hi hi cold and lonely,
Well you can syndicate any boat you row,
Yes you can syndicate any boat you row.

Anna (Go To Him)

ALBUM: Please Please Me 22.3.1963

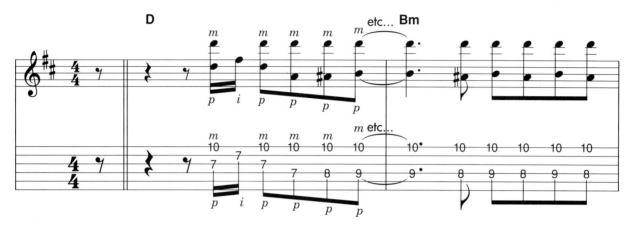

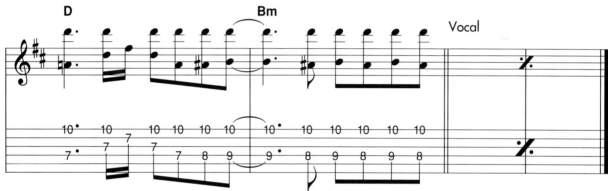

```
D        Bm              D        Bm
Anna,     you come and ask me girl
        D        Bm
To set you free, girl
                    D        Bm
You say he loves you more than me,
        Em        A
So I will set you free,
            D   Bm          D   Bm
Go with him,      go with him.

Anna girl, before you go now
I want you to know, now,
That I still love you so
But if he loves you more, go with him.

G
    All of my life I've been searching for a girl
    D
To love me like I love you oh, now,
G
    But every girl I ever had
G
    Breaks my heart and leaves me sad,
E                                    A
    What am I, what am I supposed to do
oh, oh, oh, oh, oh, oh.
```

Anna just one more thing, girl,
You give back your ring to me
And I will set you free, go with him,

All of my life
I've been searching for a girl
To love me like I love you,
But let me tell you now.

But every girl I ever had
Breaks my heart
And leaves me sad,
What am I, what am I supposed to do
oh, oh, oh, oh, oh, oh.

Anna just one more thing, girl,
You give back your ring to me
And I will set you free, go with him,
Go with him.
You can go with him girl,
Go with him.

I'm Looking Through You

ALBUM: Rubber Soul 3.12.1965

*Capo on 1st fret so that it shifts key to A♭ (same as original recording)

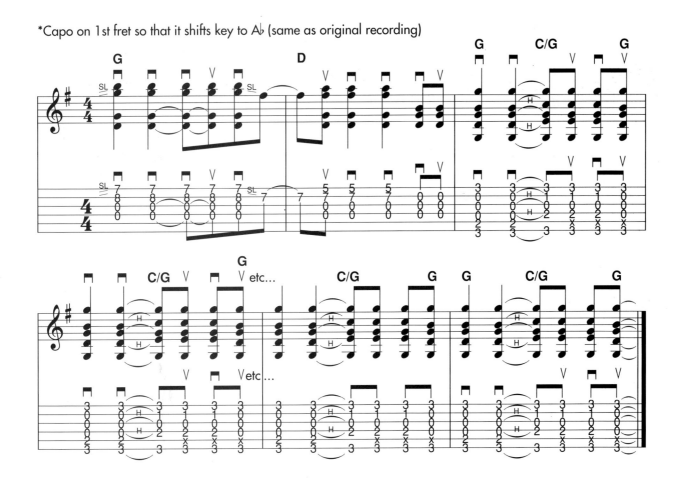

Am7   Em   D G
I'm looking through you,   where did you go?
  C   Am7   Em   D   Em
I thought I knew you,   what did I know?
                    C   G Am7 D
You don't look different, but you have changed,
G   C   Am7   C7   G
  I'm looking through you,   you're not the same.

Your lips are moving, I cannot hear,
Your voice is soothing but the words aren't clear.
You don't sound different, I've learned the game,
I'm looking through you, you're not the same.

C   G
Why, tell me why did you not treat me right?
C   G   D7
Love has a nasty habit of disappearing overnight,

You're thinking of me the same old way,
You were above me, but not today.
The only difference is you're down there.
I'm looking through you and you're nowhere.
Why tell me why did you not treat me right?
Love has a nasty habit of disappearing overnight,

I'm looking through you, where did you go?
I thought I knew you, what did I know?
You don't look different, but you have changed,
I'm looking through you, you're not the same.

You're not the same
Yeah oh, baby you've changed.
Aah I'm looking through you
Yeah I'm looking through you
You've changed, you've changed, you've changed,
You've changed.

Dizzie Miss Lizzie

ALBUM: Help 6.5.1965

Things We Said Today

SINGLE: A Hard Day's Night/Things We Said Today 10.7.1964
ALBUM: A Hard Day's Night 10.7.1964

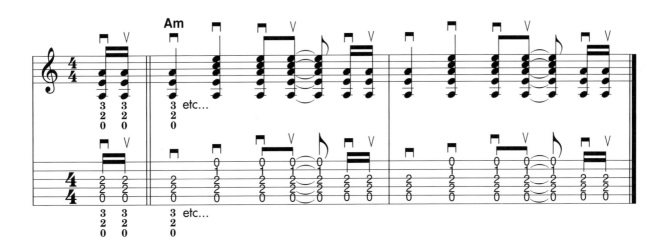

Dizzie Miss Lizzie

E7   A
You make me dizzy Miss Lizzy
The way you rock and roll.
                        D
You make me dizzy Miss Lizzy
                    A
When we do the stroll,
                E7
Come on Miss Lizzy
D   A
Love me 'fore I grow too old.

Come on give me fever
Put your little hand in mine girl,
You make me dizzy dizzy Lizzy,
Oh girl you look so fine,
Just a-rocking and a-rolling
Girl I said I wish you were mine.

You make me dizzy Miss Lizzy
When you call my name.
Ooo baby
Say you're driving me insane.
Come on, come on, come on, come on baby,
I want to be your loving man,

Run and tell your mama
I want you to be my bride.
Run and tell your brother,
Baby don't run and hide.
You make me dizzy Miss Lizzy girl,
I want to marry you.

Come on, give me fever,
Put your little hand in mine.
You make me dizzy dizzy Lizzy,
Girl you look so fine,
You're just a-rocking and a-rolling
Ooo I said I wish you were mine.

Things We Said Today

Am   Em7   Am Em7 Am Em7   Am Em7
You say you will love   me   if I have to go,

Am   Em7   Am Em7 Am   Em7   Am
You'll be thinking of   me, somehow I will know,

C7   F   Bb
Someday when I'm lonely, wishing you weren't so far away,

Am   Em7   Am Em7 Am   Em7   Am
Then I will remem - ber   things we said today.

You say you will be mine, girl, till the end of time,
These days such a kind girl seems so hard to find,
Someday when we're dreaming, deep in love, not a lot to say,
Then I will remember things we said today.

A   D7
Me I'm just the lucky kind,
A7   E7   A
Love to hear you say that love is love,
                D7
And though we may be blind,
B7   Bb
Love is here to stay.

And that's enough to make you mine girl, believe only one,
Love me all the time girl, we'll go on and on,
Someday when we're dreaming, deep in love, not a lot to say,
Then we will remember things we said today.

Blackbird

ALBUM: The Beatles 22.11.1965

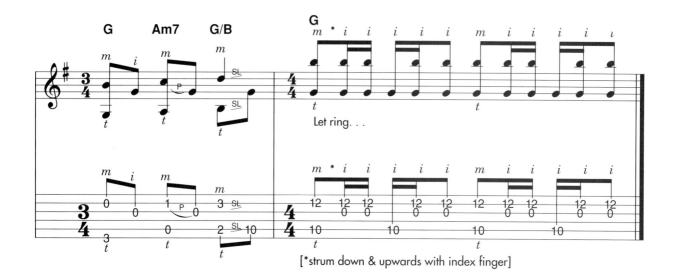

[*strum down & upwards with index finger]

```
  G        C              G
Blackbird singing in the dead of night
        A7     Am7    Adim  Em Cm
Take these broken wings and learn to fly.
  G A7 C Cm G          A7        Cm  D7 G
All your life     you were only waiting for this moment to arise.
```

Blackbird singing in the dead of night
Take these sunken eyes and learn to see.
All your life you were only waiting for this moment to be free.

```
  F       B♭ C F       B♭ A7
Blackbird fly,   blackbird fly
        D7               G C G C G
Into the light of the dark black night.
```

Blackbird fly, blackbird fly
Into the light of the dark black night.

Blackbird singing in the dead of night
Take these broken wings and learn to fly.
All your life you were only waiting for this moment to arise,
You were only waiting for this moment to arise,
You were only waiting for this moment to arise.

One After 909

ALBUM: Let It Be 8.5.1970

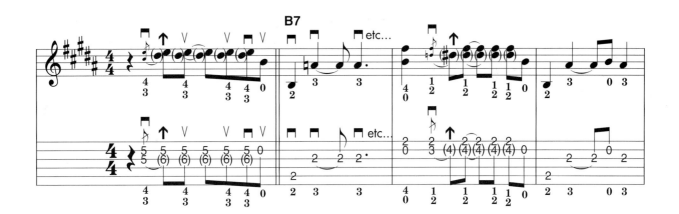

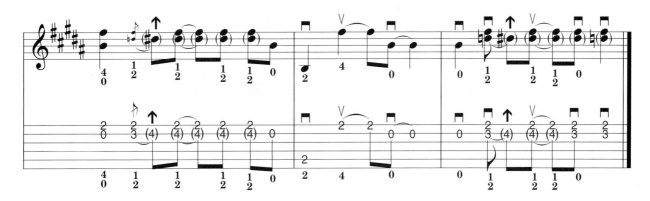

B7
My baby says she's trav'ling on the One after
Nine-O-Nine,
    B7
I said move over honey I'm travelling on that line.
   B7(♯9)   **B7(♯9)**
I said move over once, move over twice,
E7
Come on baby don't be cold as ice.
B7   **F♯7**   **B7**
I said I'm trav'ling on the One after Nine-O-Nine.

I begged her not to go and I begged her on my
bended knees,
You're only fooling around, you're fooling around
with me.
I said move over once, move over twice,
Come on baby don't be as cold as ice.
I said I'm trav'ling on the One after Nine-O-Nine.
E7   **C7**
I've got my bag, run to the station.
C♯7   **F♯7**
Railman says you've got the wrong location.
E7   **C7**
Picked up my bags, run right home.
C♯7   **F♯7**
Then I find I've got the number wrong, well,

I said I'm trav'ling on the One after
Nine-O-Nine.
I said move over honey I'm travelling on that line.
I said move over once, move over twice,
Come on baby don't be cold as ice.
I said we're trav'ling on the One after Nine-O,
I said we're trav'ling on the One after Nine-O,
I said we're trav'ling on the One after Nine-O-Nine.

A: 'Two Of Us'; 'Dig A Pony';
'Across The Universe'; 'I Me Mine';
'Dig It'; 'Let It Be'; 'Maggie Mae'.

B: 'I've Got A Feeling'; 'The One After 909';
'The Long And Winding Road'; 'For You Blue';
'Get Back'.

Let It Be, 8 May 1970, Apple [Parlophone]
PMC 7096 (stereo only).

The Night Before

ALBUM: Help 6.5.1965

D   **C** **G**   **A**
We said our goodbyes, (ah the night before)
D   **C** **G**   **A**
Love was in your eyes, (ah the night before)
Bm   **Gm6 Bm**   **Gm6**
Now today I find, you have changed your mind,
D   **G7**   **D**
Treat me like you did   the night before   yeah.

Were you telling lies (on the night before)?
Was I so unwise (on the night before)?
When I held you near, you were so sincere,
Treat me like you did the night before.

Am   **D**   **G**   **G/C** **G**
Last night is the night I will remember you by,
Bm   **E7**   **A7**
When I think of things   we did it makes me wanna cry.

We said our goodbyes, (ah the night before)
Love was in your eyes, (ah the night before)
Now today I find you have changed your mind,
Treat me like you did the night before.

Last night is the night I will remember you by,
When I think of things we did it makes me wanna cry.

Were you telling lies (on the night before)?
Was I so unwise (ah the night before)?
When I held you near, you were so sincere,
Treat me like you did the night before.
Like the night before.

Get Back

SINGLE: Get Back/Don't Let Me Down 11.4.1969

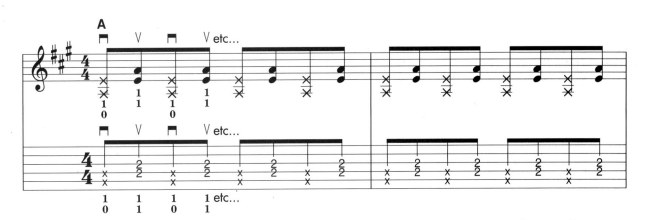

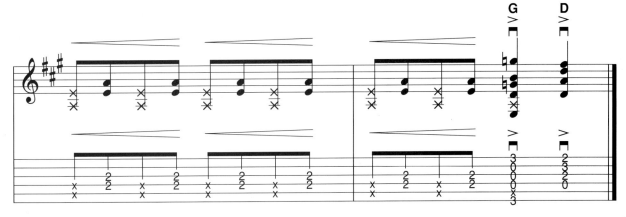

A
Jojo was a man who thought he was a loner
D   **A**
But he knew it couldn't last.
Jojo left his home in Tucson, Arizona
D   **A**
For some California grass.
       A7
Get back,   get back,
       D   **A**
Get back   to where you once belonged.
Get back, get back,
Get back to where you once belonged.

Get back Jojo. Go home,
Get back, get home,
Back to where you once belonged.
Get back, get back,
Back to where you once belonged.
Get back Jo.

Sweet Loretta Martin thought she was a woman
But she was another man.
All the girls around her say she's got it coming
But she gets it while she can.

Get back, get back,
Get back to where you once belonged.
Get back, get back,
Get back to where you once belonged.

Get back Loretta. Go home,
Get back, get back,
Get back to where you once belonged.
Get back, get back,
Get back to where you once belonged.
Get back Loretta.

THE CHARTS   23 APRIL 1969

1 GET BACK   The Beatles with Billy Preston.............
2 THE ISRAELITES   Desmond Dekker and the Aces.............
3 GOODBYE   Mary Hopkin..........
4 PINBALL WIZARD   The Who ....
5 GENTLE ON MY MIND   Dean Martin............
6 I HEARD IT THROUGH THE GRAPEVINE   Marvin Gaye ....
7 BOOM BANG-A-BANG   Lulu ....
8 COME BACK AND SHAKE ME   Clodagh Rodgers ....
9 WINDMILLS OF YOUR MIND   Noel Harrison............
10 IN THE BAD BAD OLD DAYS   The Foundations............

43 I've Just Seen A Face

ALBUM: Rubber Soul 3.12.1965

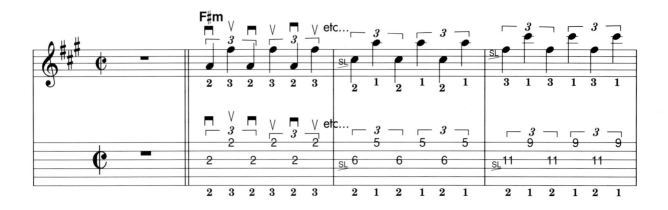

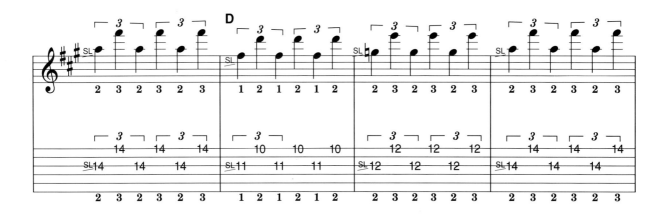

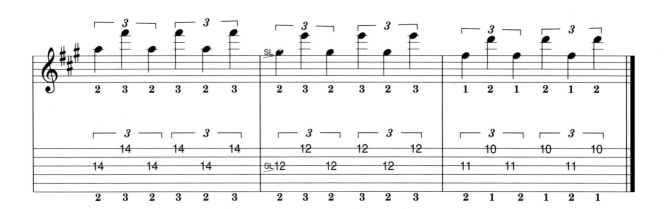

I've Just Seen A Face

Beatles For Sale, 4 December 1964, Parlophone PMC 1240 (mono), PCS 3062 (stereo).

A   Cm   Fm
I've just seen a face I can't forget the time or place where we just met,

                                           D   A
She's just the girl for me and I want the world to see we've met. Mm mm mm.

A
Had it been another day I might have looked the other way and

Fm   D   A
I'd have never been aware but as it is I'll dream of her tonight. La la la.

E   D   A   D   A
Falling, yes I'm falling, and she keeps calling   me back again.

I have never known the like of this I've been alone and I have,
Missed things and kept out of sight for other girls were never quite like this. Da da da.

Falling, yes I'm falling, and she keeps calling me back again.
Yeah, pa pa pa pa.
Falling, yes I'm falling, and she keeps calling me back again.

44   Every Little Thing

ALBUM: Beatles For Sale 4.12.1964

Rubber Soul, 3 December 1965, Parlophone PMC 1267 (mono), PCS 3075 (stereo).

Every Little Thing

A   Bm7 E7
  When I'm walking beside her,
A   D
  People tell me I'm lucky,
Bm7   E7   A
  Yes I know I'm a lucky guy.

I remember the first time
I was lonely without her,
Yes, I'm thinking about her now.

A   G   A
  Ev'ry little thing she does, she does for me, yeh,
                     G   A
And you know the things she does, she does for me, oh.

When I'm with her I'm happy,
Just to know that she loves me,
Yes I know that she loves me now.

There is one thing I am sure of,
I will love her forever,
For I know love will never die.

Ev'ry little thing she does,
She does for me, yeh,
And you know the things she does,
She does for me, oh.

Ev'ry little thing she does,
She does for me, yeh,
And you know the things she does,
She does for me, oh.

Birthday

ALBUM: The Beatles 22.11.1965

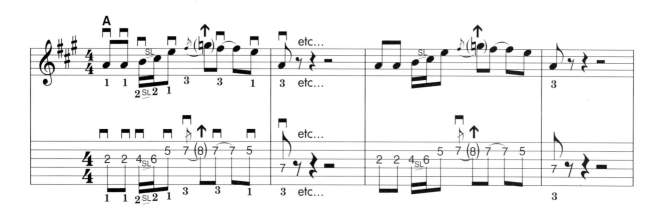

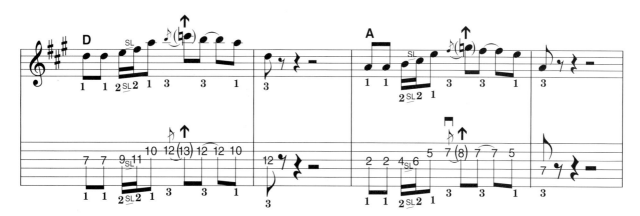

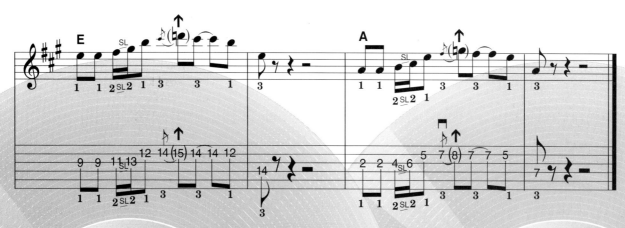

A: 'Back In The USSR'; 'Dear Prudence'; 'Glass Onion'; 'Ob-La-Di, Ob-La-Di'; 'Wild Honey Pie'; 'The Continuing Story Of Bungalow Bill'; 'While My Guitar Gently Weeps'; 'Happiness Is A Warm Gun'.

B: 'Martha My Dear'; 'I'm So Tired'; 'Blackbird'; 'Piggies'; 'Rocky Raccoon'; 'Don't Pass Me By'; 'Why Don't We Do It In The Road'; 'I Will'; 'Julia'.

The Beatles, 22 November 1968, Apple [Parlophone] PMC 7067-7068 (mono), PCS 7067-7068 (stereo).

A: 'Birthday'; 'Yer Blues'; 'Mother Nature's Son'; 'Everybody's Got Something To Hide Except Me And My Monkey'; 'Sexy Sadie'; 'Helter Skelter'; 'Long Long Long'.

B: 'Revolution I'; 'Honey Pie'; 'Savoy Truffle'; 'Cry Baby Cry'; 'Revolution 9'; 'Good Night'.

I Need You

ALBUM: Help 6.5.1965

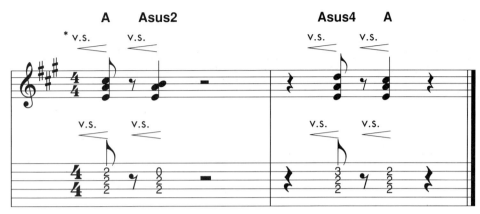

    A   Asus2   Asus4   A

* volume swell = bring volume pot. up

Birthday

A7
    You say it's your birthday.
                    D7
It's my birthday too - yeah.
                  A7
They say it's your birthday.
                    E7
We're gonna have a good time.
D7   **A7**
I'm glad it's your birthday
                  A7
Happy birthday to you.

D7
    Yes we're going to a party party,
Yes we're going to a party party.
                    C
Yes we're going to a party party.
G7
I would like you to dance - (birthday),
C **G7**   **C**
   Take a cha-cha-cha-chance - (birthday),
  G7   **C**   **Em G**
I would like you to dance - (birthday) ooh dance.

You say it's your birthday.
It's my birthday too - yeah.
You say it's your birthday.
We're gonna have a good time.
I'm glad it's your birthday
Happy birthday to you.
Happy birthday to you.

I Need You

A   **D**   **A**
You don't realise how much I need you,
                  D   **A**
Love you all the time and never leave you,
   F♯m   **Cm**
Please come on back to me,
   F♯m   **Bm**
I'm lonely as can be,
     A
I need you.

Said you had a thing or two to tell me,
How was I to know you would upset me,
I didn't realise as
I looked in your eyes,
you told me.

               D
Oh yes you told me
     E7   **A**
You don't want my lovin' anymore.
                   D   **E7**   **A**
That's when it hurt me and feeling like this
B7   **Bm7** **E7**
I just can't go on anymore.

Please remember how I feel about you,
I could never really live without you,
So, come on back and see
Just what you mean to me,
I need you, I need you, I need you.

47

Baby's In Black
ALBUM: Beatles For Sale 4.12.1964

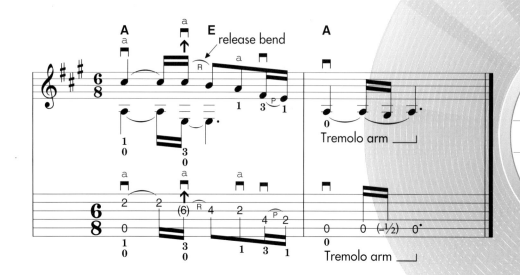

48

She Said, She Said
ALBUM: Revolver 5.8.1968

*Capo at the 1st fret to shift key to B♭ (same as original recording)

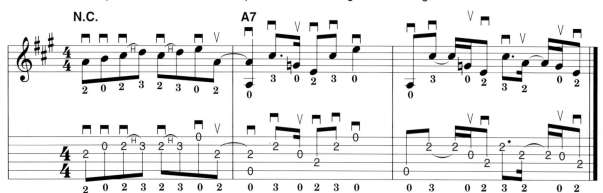

49

Till There Was You
ALBUM: With The Beatles 22.11.1963

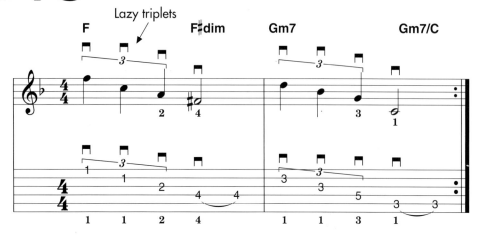

Baby's In Black

A   E7
Oh dear, what can I do?
D7   E7
Baby's in black and I'm feeling blue,
       A D7   A E7
Tell me, oh what can I do?
A   A7   D
She thinks of him and so she dresses in black,
                       A
And though he'll never come back,
E7   A
she's dressed in black.

Oh dear, what can I do?
Baby's in black and I'm feeling blue,
Tell me, oh what can I do?
I think of her, but she only thinks of him,
And though it's only a whim, she thinks of him.

F#m7   B7
Oh how long will it take,
 D   E7   A
Till she sees the mistake she has made?
Dear what can I do?
Baby's in black and I'm feeling blue,
Tell me, oh what can I do?

Oh how long will it take,
Till she sees the mistake she has made?
Dear what can I do?
Baby's in black and I'm feeling blue,
Tell me, oh what can I do?

She thinks of him and so she dresses in black,
And though he'll never come back,
she's dressed in black.
Oh dear, what can I do?
Baby's in black and I'm feeling blue,
Tell me, oh what can I do?

Till There Was You

          F   F#m
There were bells on a hill
    Gm7   B♭m7
But I never heard them ringing,
F   Am7 A♭m7 Gm7   Gm7/C
No I never heard them at all
      F   Gm7 Gm7/C
Till there was you.

There were birds in the sky
But I never saw them winging,
No I never saw them at all
Till there was you.

She Said, She Said

A   G D   A   G   D
She said   I know what it's like to be dead,
                A   G   D
I know what it is to be sad,
                 A   G   D   F G D A
And she's making me feel like I've never been born.

I said who put all those things in your hair,
Things that make me feel that I'm mad,
And you're making me feel like I've never been born.
A   G   A
She said you don't understand what I said,
     G   A   Em A
I said no no no you're wrong, when I was a boy,
                 D   A   D
Everything was right,   ev'rything was right.

I said even though you know what you know,
I know that I'm ready to leave,
'Cos you're making me feel like I've never been born.
She said you don't understand what I said,
I said no no no you're wrong, when I was a boy,
Ev'rything was right, ev'rything was right.

I said even though you know what you know,
I know that I'm ready to leave,
'Cos you're making me feel like I've never been born.
She said I know what it's like to be dead,
I know what it is to be sad,
I know what it's like to be dead.

                  B♭   B♭m
Then there was music
                 F
And wonderful roses,
   D9   Gm7 Gm7/C G7
They tell me in sweet fragrant meadows
    C   Gm7/C   C+
Of dawn   and dew.

There was love all around
But I never heard it singing,
No I never heard it at all
Till there was you.

Then there was music
And wonderful roses,
They tell me in sweet fragrant
    meadows
Of dawn and dew.

There was love all around
But I never heard it singing,
No I never heard it at all
Till there was you.
Till there was you.

With The Beatles, 22 November 1963, Parlophone PMC 1206 (mono), PCS 3045 (stereo).

A: 'It Won't Be Long'; 'All I've Got To Do'; 'All My Loving'; 'Don't Bother Me'; 'Little Child'; 'Till There Was You'; 'Please Mister Postman'.

B: 'Roll Over Beethoven'; 'Hold Me Tight'; 'You Really Got A Hold On Me'; 'I Wanna Be Your Man'; '(There's A) Devil In Her Heart'; 'Not A Second Time'; 'Money (That's What I Want)'.

Words Of Love

ALBUM: Beatles For Sale 4.12.1964

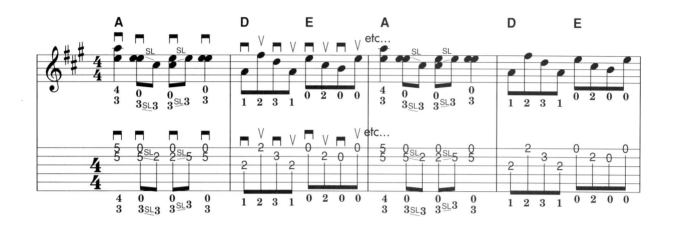

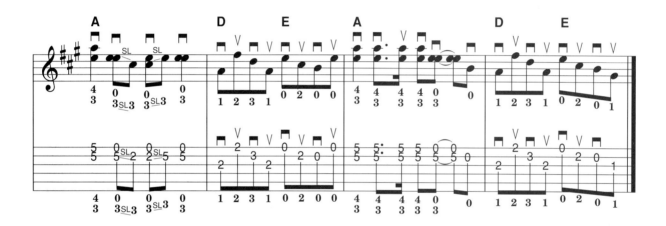

A   D E   A D
Hold me close and   tell me how you feel,
E   A D E   A D
Tell me love is real,   um um um um.

Words of love you whisper soft and true,
Darling I love you um um um um.

Let me hear you say the words I long to hear,
Darling when you're near um um um um.
Um um um um ah ah ah.